A Mother's Rights

and Other Tales

Translated by

Matina W. Muhammad

Ta-Ha Publishers Ltd.
1 Wynne Road
London SW9 0BB

Copyright © 1417/1996, Ta-Ha Publishers Ltd.

Reprinted 2003

Published by

Ta-Ha Publishers Ltd.
1 Wynne Road
London SW9 0BB

Translated by: Matina W. Muhammad
General Editor: Afsar Siddiqui
Edited by: ʿAbdassamad Clarke
Illustrated by: M. Ishaq

CIP record for this book is available from the British Library

ISBN 1 897940 49 1

Typeset by: ʿAbdassamad Clarke.

Printed in England by
Deluxe Printers, 245-a, Acton Lane,
Park Royal, London NW10 7NR

Contents

Asma's Mother

A sma ﷺ was the stepsister of A'ishah ﷺ. She was about 15 years older than her, and was married to az-Zubayr ibn al-Awwam ﷺ. Asma had become a Muslim during her life in Makkah. She had a very strong and unshakable faith.

Qateelah was her mother. She was misled and would not stop worshipping idols. The order came that kafir women could not marry or stay married to Muslim men. So Abu Bakr ﷺ asked her, "O faithful and true woman, what is your faith?" Qateelah was a woman who was very devoted to her own customs. She replied, "I will follow the way of my ancestors." Abu Bakr ﷺ decided to separate from her. She gladly went her own way.

Then the order came from Allah for the Muslims to leave Makkah. The worshippers of Allah left all their belongings, their wealth and their relations. They gathered in a town called Yathrib with groves of date palms. Soon Yathrib was renamed *Madinah an-Nabi* – the City of the Prophet ﷺ.

At the time of the Hijrah, Asma was given the title of *Dhat an-Nitaqayn* – 'The Owner of the Two Girdles'. She had torn her belt in two to tie a bag of food to her father's saddle. That was when Abu Bakr ؓ and the Prophet ﷺ had been fleeing from the Quraysh.

The people settled down in Madinah and spent some time there. Qateelah began to miss her daughter. She decided to visit her. When Asma saw her mother, she welcomed her. Then she went to the Prophet ﷺ. She wanted to find out how she should treat her. Qateelah was a kafir. She had not changed her faith and still worshipped idols.

Asma asked, "Oh Prophet of Allah, my mother has visited me. Please tell me how I should treat her." Asma wanted to know if Qateelah had any right on her children. He ﷺ told her that she had a right. The children should give her almost the same respect and honour they would give her if she was a Muslim.

Imam al-Ghazali's Mother

O nce two brothers named Ahmad and Muhammad al-Ghazali lived in the city of Tus in Khurasan. They were orphans because they had lost their father. They were brought up by their poor mother. She had to spin yarn to earn her living. She struggled hard to earn some money for their upbringing and for a good education. She tried to follow the advice of her husband to give them a good education but this was difficult without money.

A friend of their father, who was poor also, tried to help educate the boys. He did not want money for teaching. The mother still had many difficulties. But her patience was rewarded.

When he travelled in search of knowledge he wrote down everything he learnt. On a journey one day he was robbed by thieves. They took away all his goods including his precious documents. He pleaded with the leader of the robbers to return his papers. The leader said, "What kind of education did you get? Real knowledge is not in books. Real knowledge is in hearts"

The Imam was shocked. He resolved only to use the knowledge that was firmly written in his heart, not in books. Now the name of the poor yarn-spinning woman's son is recorded as one of the great sages and saints of Islam. Her son Muhammad much later became known to all the Muslims as Imam al-Ghazali 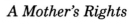.

The old mother had all her life struggled hard to bring up her sons. She died leaving behind two learned and capable Muslims. One became a jurist and the other a philosopher. They both are remembered to this day.

Mothers who raise sons like these are worthy of appreciation and honour.

A King and a Gardener

Once while a King was walking in his garden he came across an old gardener planting a seedling. He said to the gardener, "Old man, you are so old. Any day you may be taken by the angel of death. Then you will sleep the sleep of death. So why do you bother to plant this seedling?"

The old man answered, "If I am not here to see it grow I do not mind. The coming generation will see this tree fully grown and covered with fruit. They will benefit by its fruit and from its shade."

After hearing the old man, the King was overjoyed. He uttered the Persian word "Zah", which meant he was glad to hear this. He ordered that ten thousand dirhams should be given to the old gardener as a prize.

The old man was pleased to receive the prize. He said to the King, "See! My plant has already started bearing fruit. Normally a tree takes years to bear fruit. But my plant has already begun." The old man meant that the silver dirhams the King gave him

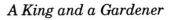

were the fruit or the result of the tree. Hearing this the King was happy and again repeated the word "Zah". He rewarded the old man with another ten thousand dirhams.

The gardener thanked the King again and said, "See, ordinarily a tree bears fruit once in every season. But this tree has borne fruit twice this season."

Imam Rabiah ar-Ray's Mother

This is another story of a very noble and famous woman whose son was Imam Rabiah ar-Ray ﵁. He was a great scholar and illustrious teacher. His students include Imam Malik ﵁ and Hasan al-Basri ﵁. His father's name was Farukh and he was a soldier in the army of Bani Umayyah. He was sent to fight in many battles.

When Imam Rabiah was born his father was often away at battles, sometimes for years at a time. In his absence Rabiah grew up to be a great scholar. Before going away, Farukh gave his wife many gold coins. She spent everything on her son's upbringing and Islamic education.

When Imam Rabiah's father came back he asked about the gold coins he had given to his wife. She answered, "They are all safe." In the meantime Imam Rabiah was giving the Khutbah and teaching students in the nearby mosque.

When Farukh came home after listening to this learned scholar he was very impressed. He had been

away such a long time that he did not recognise his own son. He told everything that he had heard the young teacher say to his wife.

Afterwards he came to know that the great shaykh and scholar was his own son, an Imam to the whole world. The Imam's father was overjoyed to hear this. He acclaimed the intelligence of his wife in the up-bringing of their son. He said, "This blessing is more to me than the many gold coins. They are now in the shape of my son Rabiah."

The mother adorned her son with high education. He was decorated with a good upbringing. It made him famous in the world forever, for his knowledge, great nobility, grace and excellence.

A Mother's Rights

A mother is responsible for the nourishment and rearing of her children. She gives up many things for her children. We should all be grateful for everything Allah has given us, including the mothers He gave us. So a mother has the following rights:

1. A mother should not be hurt, even if she has been wrong.

2. She should be respected in word and deed.

3. She should be obeyed in everything that is halal.

4. If the mother is not a Muslim, even then care should be taken for her needs. She should be given help if she is in need.

5. If she has any debts, her children should take care of them.

6. Her children should give sadaqah for her sake.

7. Her guests should be treated with kindness.

8. If the mother needs someone to attend to her, it is better to look after her than to do extra prayers and recite Qur'an. Indeed it is the same if anyone is in serious need.

9. Her children should pray for her after her death.

10. Children should visit their mother's grave and pray for her.

Here are some prayers for parents which are in the Noble Qur'an. First there is a famous prayer of the Prophet Ibrahim 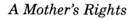:

"My Lord, make me one who establishes the prayer and also some of my descend-ants. Our Lord, accept my du'a. Our Lord, forgive me and my parents and the believ-ers on the Day when the Reckoning hap-pens." (Qur'an, Ibrahim 40-41)

There is another famous prayer for parents:

"My Lord, show mercy to the two of them just as they brought me up [when I was] small." (Qur'an, al-Isra 24)

Then there is the prayer of Sulayman ﷽:

"My Lord, inspire me to be grateful for Your blessing with which You blessed me and my parents." (Qur'an, an-Naml 19)

Women's Place in Islam

One of the Companions of the Prophet ﷺ, Asma bint Yazid al-Ansari رضي الله عنها, went to him and raised the following questions:

"O Messenger of Allah, may my father and mother be your ransom. I have come to you as a messenger from the Muslim women. Indeed, Allah has sent you as His Messenger towards both men and women. That is why we have faith in you and in Allah. But, we Muslim women are housebound and veiled, and we live in seclusion. We are always prepared to fulfil every desire of our men. We bear their children. Despite all of that, men are far ahead of us in performing acts of service to Allah. They attend the jumu'ah prayer. They join the prayers said in the mosque. They visit the sick. They attend funerals. They perform Hajj after Hajj. Moreover they go on jihad. When they go on Hajj, 'Umrah or Jihad, we women look after their homes, weave for them and raise their children. Do we not deserve the same reward from Allah as the men do?"

After listening to that, the Prophet ﷺ turned to his Companions ﵁ and said, "Do you know of any woman who is better than her in raising questions about the *deen* of Islam?"

They replied, "Messenger of Allah, we never thought that a woman would raise such a question."

Then the Prophet ﷺ turned to Asma bint Yazid and said:

"Listen carefully and understand, and then tell the women who have sent you here. A woman who is well behaved to her husband and seeks his good will and maintains it, is equal in reward to the reward of all those good deeds you have mentioned about the men."

The Allowance for Children

Once, some traders came to Madinah. When the night fell, Umar ﷺ, the second Khalifah, together with Abd ar-Rahman ibn Awf ﷺ went to guard their camp for the night. After some time they heard a child crying. Umar went to the tent and said to the child's mother, "In the name of Allah, why are you letting the child cry?"

Soon the child stopped crying. Umar went back to his guard duty. After a while the child started crying again. Umar again asked the mother not to leave the child crying. Shortly the child stopped crying and Umar returned to his guard duty.

When it happened a third time, Umar went to the mother and said, "I do not understand why you are letting the child cry. Why can't you stop it?"

The woman said to him, "It has nothing to do with you. Why are you disturbing me time and time again? I am trying to wean the child off milk."

Umar asked her, "Why do you want to do that?"

Not knowing who he was, she replied, "Umar does not pay an allowance for children who are still on mother's milk."

Umar asked her how much longer she would have to continue to feed the child. She told him that it would be for another few months. He asked her to continue to feed the child with her own milk for the full duration.

After the morning prayers, Umar ﷺ decided to extend the children's allowance to every child, from the moment of birth. He was afraid that thousands of children might have been suffering for the same reason as this one child. Then he made a declaration throughout the lands of Islam that no mother should hurry to wean her child off breast-milk, and that they would be paid the allowance from the time of birth.

Umm Salamah

Hind Umm Salamah ﷺ was an eminent Companion, who was both intelligent and beautiful. She emigrated twice – to Abyssinia and Madinah – for the sake of Allah. Her camel-borne sedan was the first to enter Madinah..

Once Umm Salamah said to her husband Abu Salamah ﷺ, "I have been told that if a woman's husband dies and he is one of the inhabitants of Paradise and she does not marry after him, Allah will join them in Paradise. And likewise, if a woman dies first and the husband is left."

She said, "I'll not marry after you."

Abu Salamah said, "Marry after me if I die first," and he prayed, "O Allah, grant Umm Salamah a better man than me and do not let her be harmed."

When Umm Salamah was nursing Abu Salamah after the Battle of Badr, he said to her, "I heard the Messenger of Allah ﷺ say, Whenever a misfortune afflicts anyone, he should say, **"Truly, we belong to**

Allah and to to Him we are returning.'" And he would pray, 'O Lord, grant me something good from it which only You, Exalted and Mighty, can give.'"

Abu Salamah fought in the Battle of Badr, in which the Muslims were victorious. In the Battle of Uhud he was severely wounded, eventually dying from those wounds. The Prophet ﷺ visited Abu Salamah ☺ during his final illness and was with him when he died.

Umm Salamah completed the waiting period of four months and ten days after the death of her husband. Then Abu Bakr ☺ proposed to her. She refused his proposal. Then Umar ☺ proposed and she turned him down too.

Then the Prophet ﷺ proposed to her. She said, "O Messenger of Allah, I have three characteristics. I am a woman who is extremely jealous. So I am afraid that you will see something in me that will anger you and Allah will punish me. I am a woman who is already advanced in age, and I am a woman who has young children."

The Prophet ﷺ replied, "As for the jealousy, I pray Allah that it will leave you. As for the question of age, I am afflicted with the same problem as you. As for your children, your family is my family."

So she married the Prophet ﷺ.

Umm Salamah was a wise woman and a good advisor. She counselled the Prophet on the Day of Hudaybiyah, when he made a treaty with the people of Makkah. The Muslims had set out to perform Umrah. They brought animals to sacrifice in Makkah. The kuffar prevented them.

Then the Prophet ﷺ made an agreement with them. He agreed not to perform the Umrah that year. Then he told the Companions ﷺ to sacrifice their animals and cut or shave their hair. Not one man got up, even after he had told them to do so three times.

They had been very shocked at how generous the Prophet ﷺ had been to the Makkans in the agreement. The Messenger of Allah ﷺ went to Umm Salamah and told her what had happened.

She said to him, "If you want them to do that, you must leave them and not say a word to any of them until you have slaughtered your animals and called your barber to shave your head."

The Prophet ﷺ followed her suggestion. He left the group of Companions without speaking to anyone. Then he slaughtered his animals and called his barber to shave his hair.

The Companions ﷺ had been too shocked to move. But when they saw this, they all arose and slaughtered their animals. They began shaving each other so eagerly that they were in danger of killing each other, out of anxiety. They were very afraid because they had not obeyed the Prophet ﷺ right away.

As a woman and a mother, Umm Salamah ﵂ had gained much wisdom. The Prophet ﷺ recognised that wisdom and trusted her. Allah showed that she was right. This is just one of the many examples of the way that the Messenger of Allah ﷺ showed honour to women and mothers.